LEAVES

In memory of Dennis Jarrett, editor and friend.

LEAVES

To: Mary Lou
Reese Taylor

Reese Taylor

Contents

7 Sainte Chapelle
9 Who Will Be Left?
11 The Rains
13 Sitting in a Stream
15 Merced Puente
19 Tales of India
21 In the Mystery
23 Hungry for Hunger
25 Fraction
27 Observing
29 Looking for Lapis Lazuli
31 The Elephant
35 El Nido Closed Today
37 Home
39 Space
41 Caro in Cordoba
45 Poems Are Like Dreams
47 Ego on My Sleeve, He Reviews
49 Donde Esta Roberto Garcia?
51 Intimate Trinket
53 Sweetness
55 Have I Been Gone Long Enough?
57 Blue Eyes There
59 Separated
61 Murder of Crows
63 Concepcion
65 You Choose
67 Live
71 Dreaming of an Avenue
75 Fear of Flying
77 Vision
81 Ego in Entourage
85 Who Will It Be?
87 Anxiety Wins
89 Cry for Protection
93 Scattered
95 Three Women Gather
97 Existential Ballet

Sainte Chapelle